COLOUR ME
SWOOOOON

Mel Elliott

PORTICO

First published in the United Kingdom in 2013 by
Portico Books
10 Southcombe Street
London
W14 0RA

An imprint of Anova Books Company Ltd

ISBN 9781909396234

A CIP catalogue record for this book is available from the British Library.

10 9 8 7 6 5 4 3 2 1

Printed and bound by 1010 Printing International Ltd, China

This book can be ordered direct from the publisher by
www.anovabooks.com

For my favourite men:
Andy, George, Charlie, Nook, Tony
and Ryan.

CONTENTS

WELCOME TO HEAVEN

If you ask me, "lust" is totally underrated. Reading highbrow newspapers and going to the la-di-da opera are all well and good, but from time to time you just need to sit back, look at some good old-fashioned beefcake and go:

"BABEEE! He's gorgeous!"

Team that up with a pile of felt-tip pens and what do you have?

HEAVEN!

IN A COLOURING BOOK!

This book will make you go weak at the knees as you and your colouring pens caress chiselled features and chest hair. From Aaron Paul to Zac Efron, all the hotties are here, and in no particular order (except for Ryan Gosling, who I put in first place because it's my book and I can, so there).

This isn't any old colouring book overflowing with gorgeous guys, though! Every hunk has a "you do it" bit where you get to do quizzes, write love poetry and, most immaturely, score each man out of ten.

You can get creative, too! Feel free to add slogans to T-shirts, patterns to ties and even add clothes if you feel that some of them are a little underdressed.

So what are you waiting for? Embrace your inner teenager! Here are a load of heartthrobs, just waiting and longing for you to "colour them good". Enjoy!

Love,

Mel

x

RYAN GOSLING

You're handsome and witty and cool as hell,
You're muscular, toned and smart as well.
You take care of your mum and you play the uke,
You make my husband want to puke.

I love you in movies by Derek Cianfrance,
And with Steve Carell, when you're missing your pants.
You're greater than Clooney and Pitt and Bale,
And Franco and Efron, to insignificance they pale!

You're colouring yourself; I hope you don't mind.
Just don't do it too often or you could go blind.
I'm sorry for that – let's please call a truce:
I'M JUST DESPERATE TO BE WITH YOU, BABY GOOSE!

Why don't you write your own poem about
Canada's finest export?
It's easy (unless you try to rhyme anything with "Gosling")!

You don't have to score Ryan out of ten; I did it for you

AARON PAUL

I'm not normally that keen on meth addicts, but Aaron Paul's character in *Breaking Bad* has the ability to make them completely adorable,* like the type of guy you'd proudly take home to meet your mum and say, "Hi, Mum. Meet my new boyfriend. He's a meth addict and he's murdered a few people, but – LOOK AT HIM!" She'd fall for him in an instant.

Aaron Paul seems like such a happy-go-lucky guy, and, being an integral part of what I believe to be the greatest TV show of all time, he should be.

You can dissolve me with hydrofluoric acid anytime, Aaron!**

I made you some
Breaking Bad anagrams!

WE MIRTH

KHAN

JEANS MEN SKIP

LAGOON MUDS

BOY ITCH

I score Aaron Paul  10

* I'm not saying that drug abuse is the way to forge loving
  relationships so don't even try it. Drugs are bad, kids.
** Not really.

GEORGE CLOONEY

George Clooney stole my heart when he saved that little boy who was stuck in a tunnel on *ER** and he jammed a biro in his neck. What a hero!

ACROSS
(2) Which country does George survey via satellite?
(4) Name the actor who plays Dr John Carter, George's colleague on *ER*.
(7) Name George's character in *The Ides of March*.
(8) Name the 2012 movie starring Ben Affleck that was co-produced by Clooney.
(9) Name the hospital drama in which George shot to fame.

DOWN
(1) The first name of the female actress who co-starred with George in two films.
(3) The first name of George's famous aunt.
(5) Name the Italian lake where George owns a house.
(6) Name the brother directors responsible for three George Clooney roles.

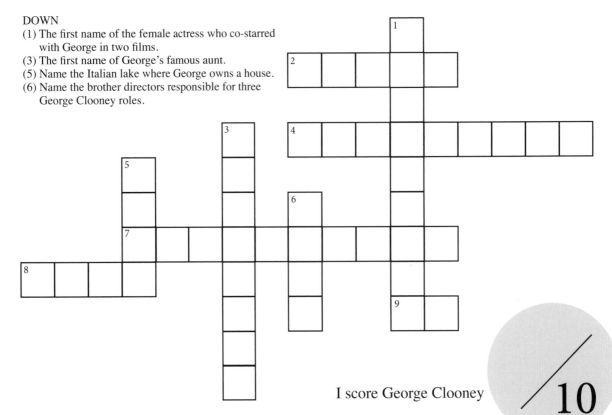

I score George Clooney /10

* "Hell and High Water" episode.

BEN AFFLECK

It's not often that a sequel is better than the original, but Bennifer 2 is undoubtedly the exception.

Since becoming a husband and father, and growing his lucky beard, Ben Affleck has gone from boy to "What a man!" Right now, he's probably putting together flat-packed trophy cases for all his awards. No doubt he stays dressed in his tux these days just in case he has a last-minute award to collect!

But besides being lucky for him, the beard, tux *and* maturity suit him so well that he *had* to appear in *Colour Me Swoooooon*!

> The thing I like most about Ben Affleck is:
> (a) His lucky beard
> (b) His BFF (George Clooney)
> (c) His speeches
> (d) I don't care about the beard and all the awards – I still don't like him.
>   I'd rather listen to "Jenny from the Block".

I score Ben Affleck   /10

JAMES FRANCO

I asked my Facebook friends and Twitter followers to describe
James Franco ... and I put the results into a word search. Enjoy!

```
S R E K N O B Y B K B Z T K E O I W I F A K L
O H E E D I Z E B S E C G T N A U N O I G L P
C H I M P H W N F L S X Q X J B V M E T V B T
B S K E D S Y O A O C H S O C N N O O O T S N
S X J M U J X O L O H N O O A O F E W T H V A
V E E T Y S J L R X G X Z H R G I O O X I S I
S P X K E E R C M A H Q T D X C K F R Y D K L
N L C Y O X I A H L R R B J Y U Q W G A E M L
M O R N C S Z N Z X E R Y I Y O L Q M U V C I
C D B A W C G N H T K C O U X Q B A D T I E R
E T G K H Y D O T S Z T K G X P Z D Q E L E B
E R F L O I T Y O P E O M E A I P D A L I L T
L J A B ? F B I Q W F P F E N N E H Q B S O L
O G P K Q M Y N H X V S K G T C T U N I H H P
O Z I J F D P G Z G J G E D S N R X A D W H O
A F T E R S H A V E D U D E S O L M U E Y J U
J I H U J S D M U K K U V Q C Y Y T G Q H G T
G O R G E O U S Y F I D I R T Y W S H X K P N
L C N H E R Q Q J R D S P W E F O U T F K S L
S L K V P T R N N L M T Y Y Z P X X Y V S Z L
```

AMAZING
BAD BOY
AFTERSHAVE DUDE
ARROGANT
FIT
NAUGHTY
DEVILISH
COCKY
HOT
SEXY
DIRTY
ANNOYING
EDIBLE
WHO?
BONKERS
GORGEOUS
BRILLIANT

I would like to give James Franco /10

PRINCE HARRY

Hardly the unknown soldier, Prince Harry is the hottest member of the British Royal Family since one of them scalded themselves in the bath.

For an aristocrat, he has a wicked sense of humour, has the cheekiest of twinkles in his eyes and is adored by girls and women all over the world.

If you fancy your chances of becoming the next British princess, head down to the cool clubs of Kensington, London, look out for the ginger Prince, polish your tiara, use one of the following pick-up lines, and ...
GOOD LUCK!*

"Is that a mirror in your pocket? Because I can see myself in your pants."

"Are you free tonight, or will it cost me?"

"You're so hot that when I look at you I get a tan."

If none of the above works, simply tell him he's only fourth in line
to the throne and can't afford to be picky.

I'd give Prince Harry a right royal  10

* You'll need it!

ZAC EFRON

From the moment he jazz-handedly leaped onto our screens in 2006, women everywhere felt a guilty flutter of excitement. Oh yes, he knew all the moves (and, in true musical style, so did the rest of the school).

However, Zac Efron was officially too young for us, so we kept our feelings under wraps until he sprouted a bit of chin hair and made it legally acceptable for us to fancy him. But now he's *out* of high school and what a fine young man he's turned out to be. Along with his hair, his career is going from strength to strength, with challenging and stylish roles – and I'm sure he can still do a backflip or two when it's called for.

Zac is reported as saying, "I like my women like I like my peanut butter: chunky." And, Zac, I like my men like I like my cream doughnuts: yellow and thick. Er, so I guess I'll be calling Homer Simpson (note to self: work on similes!).

> The thing I like most about Zac Efron is:
> (a) The cut of his jib
> (b) His hair
> (c) Nothing, he's not my cup of tea
> (d) ....

I would give Zac Efron

BRADLEY COOPER

Bradley Cooper: he's such a "guy", isn't he? Men want to have a beer with him and women want to have his babies.

I have kindly made anagrams of some films that feature Bradley Cooper:

VEGAN HER HOT

DATELINES NAVY

SANE MY

A EH SHUTOUT JOINT SNOTTY

VALUABLE TOTES

ED THROWS

A BELLYING VIOLINS PORKS

Can you work out what they are?

If you were forcing me to rate Bradley Cooper, I'd give him 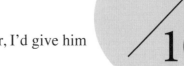 10

JAVIER BARDEM

No one does baddies quite like Javier.

Whether he's sporting a classic bob in *No Country for Old Men*, or an albino pixie cut in *Skyfall*, Javier knows how to give audiences the creeps. However, let him act in his own hair and he's tastier than the tastiest paella.

If you'd like to sip sangria with Mr Bardem, give yourself a fighting chance by learning these useful Spanish phrases:

Mi reloj mágico dice que usted no está usando ninguna ropa interior!
Debe ser un ayuno hora.
My magical watch says you're not wearing any underwear.
Must be an hour fast!

Tiene algún pasas? No? Qué tal una fecha, entonces?
Do you have any raisins? No? How about a date then?

Hay algo malo con mi móvil. No tiene su número en él.
There's something wrong with my phone. It doesn't have your number in it.

Te apetece una copa y un kebab?
Fancy a beer and a kebab?

I give Javier Bardem (with normal hair)  10

CHANNING TATUM

I have only ever seen two Channing Tatum movies, which to be honest were
made for pubescent boys, and I never really understood the fuss over him.
However, having just watched the trailers for *The Vow* and *Dear John*,
I'm all teary eyed, ready to see more and wanting to jump right on board
the Tatum Express to Loveville!

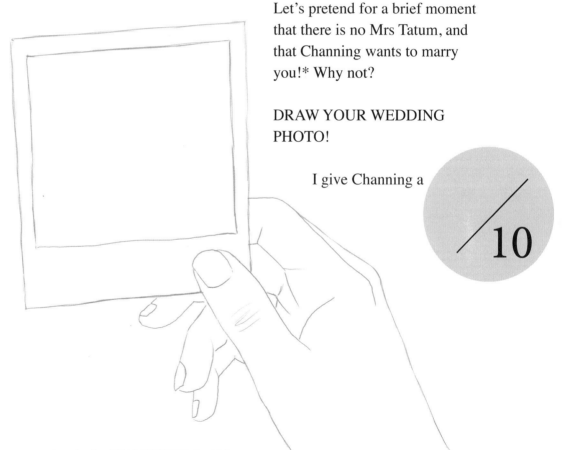

Let's pretend for a brief moment
that there is no Mrs Tatum, and
that Channing wants to marry
you!* Why not?

DRAW YOUR WEDDING
PHOTO!

I give Channing a

/10

* You're going to have to use your imagination REALLY HARD for this!

DAVID BECKHAM

I asked some close friends to give me the first word that popped into their heads when I said, "David Beckham". Find their answers in the word search.

```
P C D Z P Y B Z U Q E
V H I B A U D H N G T
T A W U C M E V D R A
A R T O K M T I E S B
T I W X A Y A C R T R
T T A O G A R T W N U
O A T Z E X R O E A T
O B K N U H E R A P S
E L P M I S V I R Y A
D E C D A D O A H R M
```

CHARITABLE   UNDERWEAR   MASTURBATE*
HUNK   YUMMY   DAD
SIMPLE   OVERRATED   PACKAGE
VICTORIA   TATTOOED   PHWOAARRR

David always scores

10

GERARD BUTLER

Gerard Butler is a much better actor than people give him credit for. A couple of his Hollywood roles have left me utterly bewildered, but, having watched *The Jury* (a BBC miniseries) and a short film titled *Please*, it's pretty easy to see how he went from bonny Scotland to Hollywood in the first place.

Tell me what you would make Gerard wear if he were your ACTUAL butler …

....

....

… and what would you make him do?

....

....

I'd like to give Gerard Butler

10

JAKE GYLLENHAAL

The following are all anagrams of films starring
Jake Gyllenhaal. Do you know what they are?

A FREEDOM WORTHY TROAT

AND DRY NOOK

A KEBAB CROUTON MINK

RESCUED COO

A TODDLERS HUNGOVER

RIGHTED GO LO

I score Jake Gyllenhaal  /10

PHARRELL WILLIAMS

Picture the scene: Pharrell Williams is all like, "Yo [insert your name here] ...., you wanna come party wit' me later?" And you're like, "Hell to the yeah, Pharrell!"

On my date with Pharrell I want to go to [restaurant] ....

I am going to wear ....

I am going to order [draw your dinner on the plate]

Then we will go to [bar/club]

....

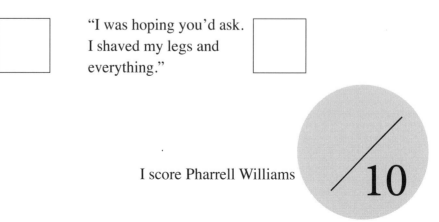

If Pharrell invites me back to his crib
I will say (tick as appropriate):

"That's awfully kind of
you, Pharrell, but I'm
going to decline. I have to
be up early in the morning
to do some stuff."

"I was hoping you'd ask.
I shaved my legs and
everything."

I score Pharrell Williams   /10

TOM HARDY

This guy has the beefiest lips I have never encountered, unfortunately.

He is also, in my opinion, the best actor in this book, with many flawless performances under his belt. He seems to give every part "his all" to make the characters he plays, whether fictional or not, completely believable.

Tom has not led a sheltered life, and it shows – in a really nice way. He thrives on his faults and imperfections, making them work in his favour and using his personal experiences to help others.

I have seen three Tom Hardy films now where he is completely unattractive, and, while that's a shame for someone so handsome, it's also a huge reflection on his talent.

I dream one day of a movie starring Tom Hardy and Ryan Gosling. I would watch that movie *a lot*.

Why don't you think of a great movie idea starring Tom and Ryan, pitch it to a few directors, and invite me to the première?

Tom gets a hardy

10

RYAN REYNOLDS

Ryan Reynolds is so deliciously chiselled that he actually looks like someone has carved him out of toffee. The only downside is that he might stick to your teeth.

Ryan has a wonderful, self-deprecating sense of humour. He also has an incredibly beautiful wife, so I think our chances with him are slim to zero, but, if he *didn't* have a very beautiful wife and you were about to become the next Mrs Reynolds, what would be on your wedding registry? A toaster? A massage chair? Some colouring books? Go through your favourite catalogues, cut out your wish list, and glue it on this page (don't be *completely* selfish; think about what Ryan would want, too).

Ryan rates  10

CHRISTIAN BALE

My favourite Christian Bale role of all time has to be the super-ironic *American Psycho*, with its '80s glamour, Genesis soundtrack and gruesome murders. I loved this movie so much I was compelled to write this poem about him.

All hail Christian Bale.
When I marry you I will wear a veil.
My skin will be tanned and my dress will be pale.
I'll be the world's happiest female,
and on our honeymoon, away we will sail.
Apologies for this epic poem fail,
Christian Bale.

See if you can write a Christian Bale love poem that is even worse than this one!
(Try to rhyme the last word of each line.)

....

....

....

Christian Bale deserves / 10

ALEXANDER SKARSGÅRD

Alexander Skarsgård is a Swedish actor who loves to sink his teeth into roles. He shot to fame as Eric Northman in *True Blood* where he plays a Viking vampire with control issues.

ALEX FACTS:

- He had ambitions to be a rock star.
- His favourite colour is "rainbow coloured".
- If he could play any part in *Star Wars* he would be Chewbacca.

Below are some great pick-up lines to use on Swedish vampires. Practise them just in case you are ever lucky enough to meet Alex!

Bit mig, Alex!
Bite me, Alex!

Vilken snygg skjorta, den skulle gå bra ihop med mitt golv.
That's a nice shirt, it would go well with my floor.

Jag lagar middag om du lagar frukost.
I'll cook dinner if you cook breakfast.

Är det där vampyrtänder, eller är du bara glad att se mig?
Are those fangs or are you just happy to see me?

Alex Skarsgård scores  10

PATRICK DEMPSEY

THE best proposal of marriage I have ever seen was performed by Patrick Dempsey in *Sweet Home Alabama,* and I think Reese Witherspoon was "withouterbrain" not to go back to New York with him.

Since Reese left him, Patrick trained to be a "smooth operator" – and what a fine and charismatic doctor he is.

Pretend you're on *Grey's Anatomy* and you're desperate to be seen by Dr Shepherd. What disease are you going to make up?

My disease is called

....

It hurts here

My symptoms are

....

I think the best way to cure it is to

....

Draw the part of your body where it hurts.

HUGH JACKMAN

Get to know Hugh better – complete this crossword!

ACROSS
(5) With (3) down.
(6) With (4) down.
(8) 2008 movie about his homeland.
(10) French revolution musical.
(11) With (10) across.

DOWN
(1) Cheerful penguin movie voiced by Jackman.
(2) Hugh's *X Men* character.
(3) 2004 *Dracula* movie.
(4) Hugh went all magical in 2006.
(7) Hugh's birth city.
(9) With (1) down.

I score Hugh Jackman  /10

DAMIAN LEWIS

Damian Lewis is the British *Homeland* actor who has a better American
accent than many Americans.

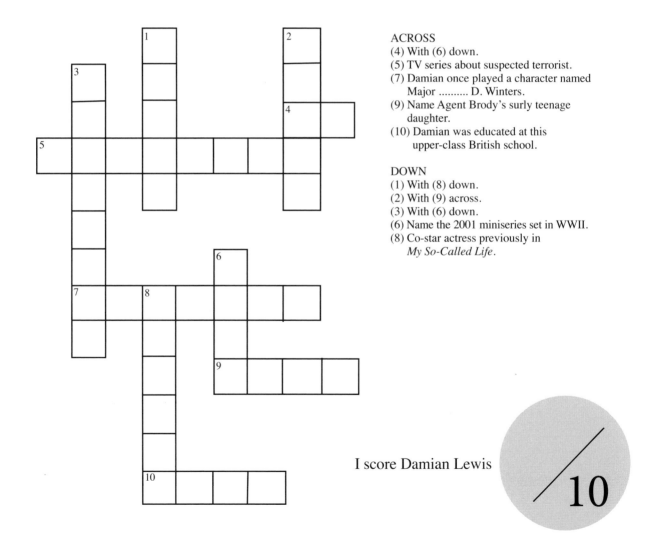

ACROSS
(4) With (6) down.
(5) TV series about suspected terrorist.
(7) Damian once played a character named
    Major .... D. Winters.
(9) Name Agent Brody's surly teenage
    daughter.
(10) Damian was educated at this
    upper-class British school.

DOWN
(1) With (8) down.
(2) With (9) across.
(3) With (6) down.
(6) Name the 2001 miniseries set in WWII.
(8) Co-star actress previously in
    My So-Called Life.

I score Damian Lewis   / 10

Brad scores

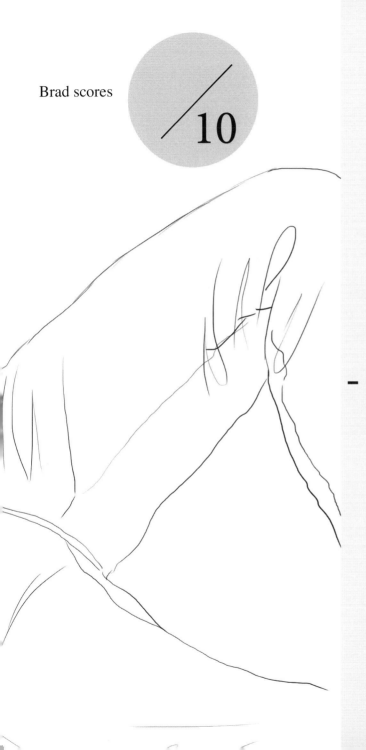

/10

BRAD PITT

Brad Pitt is so good-looking that he simply *had* to become an actor – either that or a male escort (personally, I think he made the right choice).

In the 1995 movie *Se7en*, Pitt plays a young cop trying to track down a serial killer obsessed with the seven deadly sins.

Serious self-analysing task: how do the seven deadly sins manifest themselves within you?

Cut out & take to your therapist.

LUST ....

GLUTTONY ....

GREED ....

SLOTH ....

WRATH ....

ENVY ....

PRIDE ....

JUSTIN TIMBERLAKE

The following images depict something to do with JT.
Can you guess what they are?

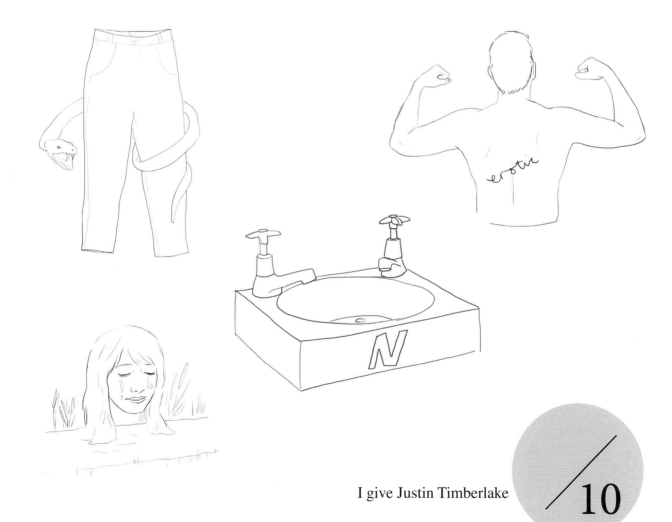

I give Justin Timberlake
/10

BENEDICT CUMBERBATCH

Benedict Timothy Carlton Cumberbatch has the best celebrity name since Engelbert Humperdinck and is the only actor I know who looks a little bit like an otter.* If you're casting someone to play a mad genius, then Benedict is your man. His choices to portray Stephen Hawking, Vincent Van Gogh and Sherlock Holmes were as smart as they are.

To get your Benedict Cumberbatch name, take the name of your first pet, add your favourite example of onomatopoeia,** take the name of your second pet, add your favourite conjunction,*** then add your favourite vegetable.

I am

TINKLEDONG FLUFFYETSPROUT

Who are you?

I give Benedict /10

* Google Benedict Cumberbatch otter.
** Onomatopoeia is the use of words that describe a sound, like *buzz* or *hum*.
*** A conjunction is a word commonly known as a "linking word", like *and* or *but*.

WENTWORTH MILLER

Ask any woman for her top ten men and Wentworth Miller is usually in there somewhere. He shot to fame playing Michael Scofield, a cunningly tattooed escapologist in *Prison Break*, but, to me, his best talent is looking much younger than his age.

In the show, Wentworth's perfect torso was covered in cleverly disguised diagrams of the prison building he was incarcerated in – but that's all kind of boring.

Why don't you use my drawing opposite and cover Wentworth in tattoos of your choice? You can put your name, your favourite band or just some pretty drawings of swallows and anchors.

I have kindly started you off!

I score Wentworth Miller  10

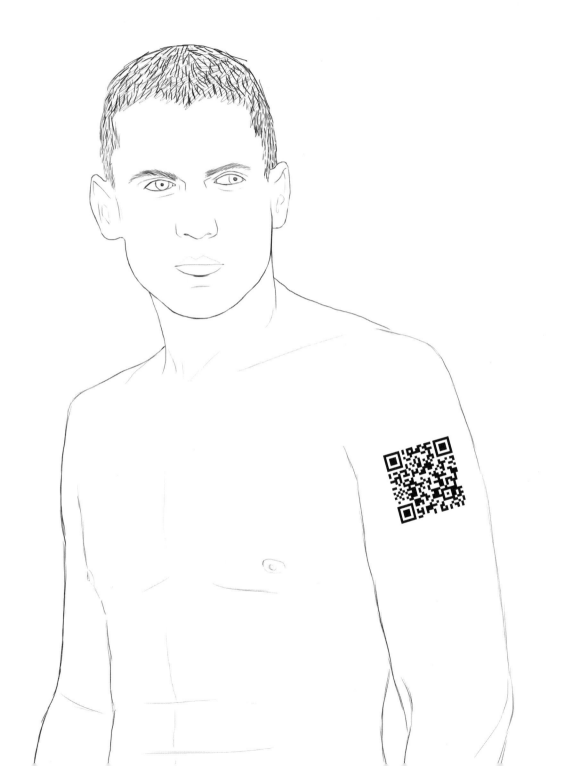

JARED LETO

Jordan Catalano, how I adored thee. You were the hottest Jordan since New Kids on the Block. With your exotic name and your brooding good looks, you were the high school heartbreaker, and it's no surprise that Claire Danes went a bit crazy.*

Yes, before getting all goth-rock and Twitter-heavy, the lovely Jared Leto played the love interest of a young Claire Danes on *My So-Called Life*, and women and girls alike had Jared Leto at the top of their lists.

Jared Leto is always on Twitter, so if you want to capture his heart, why not impress him in a tweet?

Make yourself stand out using only your remaining 130 characters!

@JaredLeto

130   **Tweet**

I score Jared Leto

/10

* See *Homeland* season 1.

ONE DIRECTION

There are five members of One Direction: Harry, Harry, Harry, Harry and Harry. Just kidding. Seriously, since they were formed on *The X Factor* in 2010, I have changed my mind about who's my favourite as often as I have changed my pants.

Speaking of pants, design a pair for your favourite 1D member!

These pants have been lovingly designed for

....

If you can't decide which member of One Direction to marry, why don't you cut up some magazines and create a collage of all your favourite 1D parts?

Love Harry's curly mop but like Zayn's eyes and Louis's body?

Get out some scissors and glue and PLAY GOD!

NIALL /10   LOUIS /10

ZAYN /10   LIAM /10

HARRY /10

It's decision time. They don't want to share you. Which direction are you going to head in?

Zayn

Niall

Louis

Harry

Liam

Left to right: Zayn, Liam, Louis, Niall, Harry.

If you *still* haven't decided on your favourite, why not use the stars to determine your compatability?

Zayn & Louis = Capricorn (most compatible with Taurus & Virgo)
Liam & Niall = Virgo (most compatible with Taurus & Capricorn)
Harry = Aquarius (most compatible with Gemini & Libra)

HUGH GRANT

We cannot forget when your behaviour was "lewd",
But you're pretty smart when you're in the mood.
You've played plenty of fops in a rom-com caper,
But you kicked the ass of the crappy Sunday paper.
You've got floppy hair and you wear cool suits,
So let's go out and eat salmon en croûte.

Write your own little poem about Hugh Grant!

I think Hugh Grant should be the next British Prime Minister because:

(a) of his acting ability, especially in *Notting Hill*.

(b) of his honest apology on *The Jay Leno Show* in 1995.

(c) he already knows his way around 10 Downing Street,
    thanks to *Love Actually*.

Hugh Grant scores /10

JOAQUIN PHOENIX

Simply one of the best actors of his generation, Joaquin Phoenix made Commodus (his evil character in *Gladiator*) look like he positively pooped in his pants when Russell Crowe announced, "I am Maximus."

Several years later, he nearly *became* Johnny Cash in *Walk the Line* and later played himself on *The David Letterman Show* while making the spoof documentary *I'm Still Here*.

```
R W E X C N L N P J
P O A S A M I D O S
H R T G E U I H F U
O T N A Q E N S A D
E R Z A I N R A B O
N C O Q Y D V C R M
I J V I L L A G E M
X S N G I S D L E O
N A G T E X Y T G C
K C D C U A O L Y Z
```

Try to find these Joaquin Phoenix-related words!

CASH
COMMODUS
GLADIATOR
JOAQUIN
JOHNNY
PHOENIX
REESE
SIGNS
VILLAGE

I give Joaquin /10

GARY BARLOW

Gary, like the finest of wines, keeps getting better and better with age. Once a chubby Billy Idol look-a-like with bleached white spiky hair trying desperately to keep up with dance routines, he has gone from crapper to "dapper" with hit-after-hit songwriting skills to rival the best.

So, why not show your appreciation and write a million love songs about our Gary.

Okay, that might be a bit too much, how about just *one* love song.

Still, too much?

How about one *verse* of a love song about Mr Barlow's hair?

Okay, don't bother, just go and have a lie down and dream about him serenading you or one day calling you "babe".

If you and Gary ruled the world, what three things would you do together:

[1]

[2]

[3]

Give Gary Barlow / 10

DANIEL CRAIG

All criticisms about Daniel Craig's unworthiness as James Bond were immediately dismissed at the beginning of *Casino Royale* when he emerged from the sea in just his trunks. Women everywhere have been swooning over him ever since. His rugged good looks, ripped body and ocean-blue eyes make him one of England's hottest attractions.

lemon peel

½ measure of Kina Lillet*

1 measure of vodka

3 measures of gin

James Bond is famous for many things: his sharp suit, his inventive gadgets and his success with women. But most of all he is famous for his vodka Martinis: shaken, not stirred.

The recipe above is for a Vesper Martini, as drunk in *Casino Royale*. Enjoy!

Daniel Craig scores

/10

* Kina Lillet is often labelled as "Blanc" or "White" Lillet.

HENRY CAVILL

NAME THAT TUNE!

Dur Du Du Du Durr
Dur Dur Dur
Dur Du Du Du Durr
Dur Du-Durrrr

Are you all set to see much more of Henry?
Good! Because he's SUPERcalifragilisticexpialidocious!

British actor Henry Cavill *is* the new Superman and his
Superman costume is way better than previous on-screen
attempts. No underpants over tights for this guy – oh no!

Why not pretend you're Henry Cavill's
Superwoman. Go and design a costume fitting such
an important job! How would yours look?

I give Henry Cavill a super-duper

10

COLIN FIRTH

Colin Firth is understated, charming and exudes that typical British reserve that makes him so disarmingly attractive.

As Mr Darcy in *Pride and Prejudice*, he set pulses racing so fast that he just *had* to play the modern-day Mr Darcy in *Bridget Jones's Diary*, too!

I think I love him. Actually.

Write your own *Bridget Jones*-style diary entry for today!

....

....

....

....

....

Today, I'm giving Colin   /10

....

USHER

Usher is smoother than a new bar of soap. If you were his lady, he'd take you back to his and turn the lights down seductively low. A roaring log fire would erupt the second he clicked his fingers, and he'd have a smoochy soundtrack* ready on the decks for moments of romance.

Below are some of Usher's hits all muddled up.
But what the heck are they?

CALM XI

RANDY DIRECT

WAD ONLY YOU

EEL ME EMS

VINCIBLE OH LUS

Usher gets a super-smooth

10

* Barry White or Al Green, for example.

JOSEPH GORDON-LEVITT

My JGL crush began a few years ago, when he performed drunken Pixies karaoke in *(500) Days of Summer*. Annoyingly, I think it was also the moment that he captured Summer's heart, too, and I spent the rest of the film compulsively booing Zooey Deschanel for being so mean to him.

Luckily, he ended up meeting a lovely architect and they probably lived happily ever after in their dream house that they designed together.

Living in your little fantasy world, why don't you pretend that you're JGL's architect girlfriend, and design a love nest for you and him.

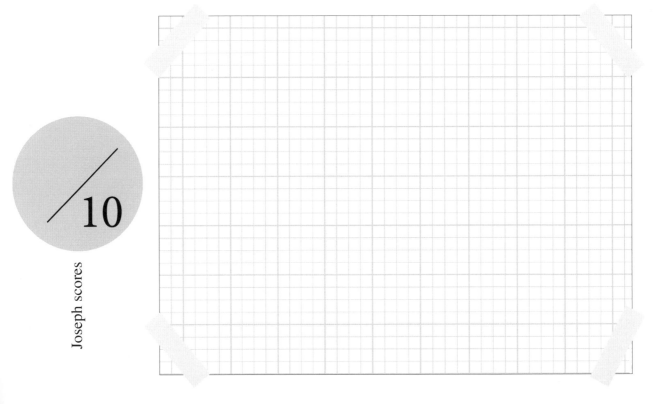

/10

Joseph scores

IDRIS ELBA

Since shooting to fame as an overambitious drug dealer and everyone's favourite bad guy on *The Wire*, Idris Elba has gone back to his London-based roots in *Luther*. Whenever you think you're tired of maverick cops on TV, another one comes along and awakens your interest. DCI John Luther is no exception. He has deep psychological issues, he doesn't play by the rules and he's on the verge of suicidal vigilantism. If you haven't seen *Luther*, give it a try!

Besides being a modern-day superhero, Idris Elba also enjoys DJ-ing, since helping his uncle start a wedding DJ business back in the 1980s.

What songs would you want Uncle Elba to play at yours and Idris's wedding?

First dance ....

One to get everyone up ....

Wedding favourite ....

Drunk & disorderly ....

Slow it down ....

Smoochy-time/slow dance ....

I score Idris Elba   / 10

1980s HEARTTHROB SPECIAL!

Featuring:

ROB LOWE

MATT DILLON

KEVIN BACON

RALPH MACCHIO

JOHN CUSACK

MICHAEL J. FOX

and

TOM SELLECK

Ah, the 1980s. When hair was spiky, shoulder pads were massive, sleeves were rolled up, and people had nothing better to do than dance. They danced in rivers, in churches (NAUGHTY Kevin!), and in school detention. But who danced their way into your heart? Let's find out ...

Rob Lowe

Best '80s moments
The Outsiders
St. Elmo's Fire
Masquerade
About Last Night

The best thing about Kevin Bacon is his

....

The thing I love most about Rob Lowe is his

....

If I could change one thing about Ralph Macchio, it would be his

....

If I could hide anything in Tom Selleck's moustache, I would hide a

....

If I could get John Cusack to say anything to me, he would say

....

The secret of Michael J. Fox's success is

....

If I had to describe Matt Dillon in three words, those words would be

....

Matt Dillon

Best '80s moments

The Outsiders
The Flamingo Kid
Rumblefish
Drugstore Cowboy

EVERYONE must know the "Footloose" dance by now! If you don't, go and learn it now, then impress people at parties for the rest of your life!

MAKE AN '80s MIXTAPE!

Grow a bushy Tom Selleck-esque moustache!

Picture the scene: you're all dressed up in your favourite mini-skirt, your hair is teased, and you're ready to party. You have the phone numbers of these seven heartthrobs ...

Who ya gonna call?

Answer ....

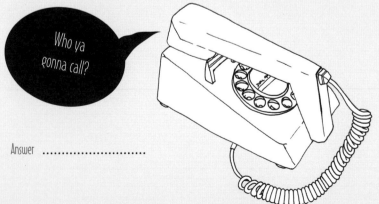

KEVIN BACON /10

ROB LOWE /10

RALPH MACCHIO /10

MICHAEL J. FOX /10

JOHN CUSACK /10

TOM SELLECK /10

MATT DILLON /10

Kevin Bacon

Best '80s moments
Diner
Footloose
She's Having a Baby

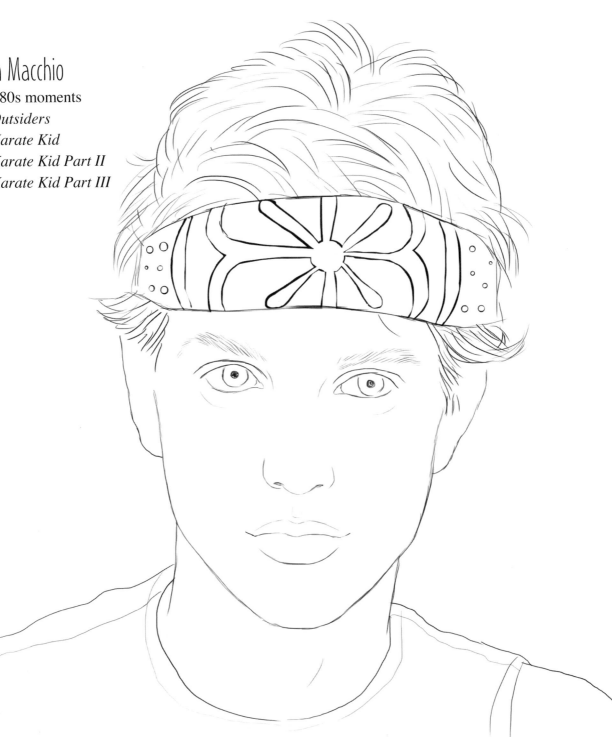

Ralph Macchio

Best '80s moments
The Outsiders
The Karate Kid
The Karate Kid Part II
The Karate Kid Part III

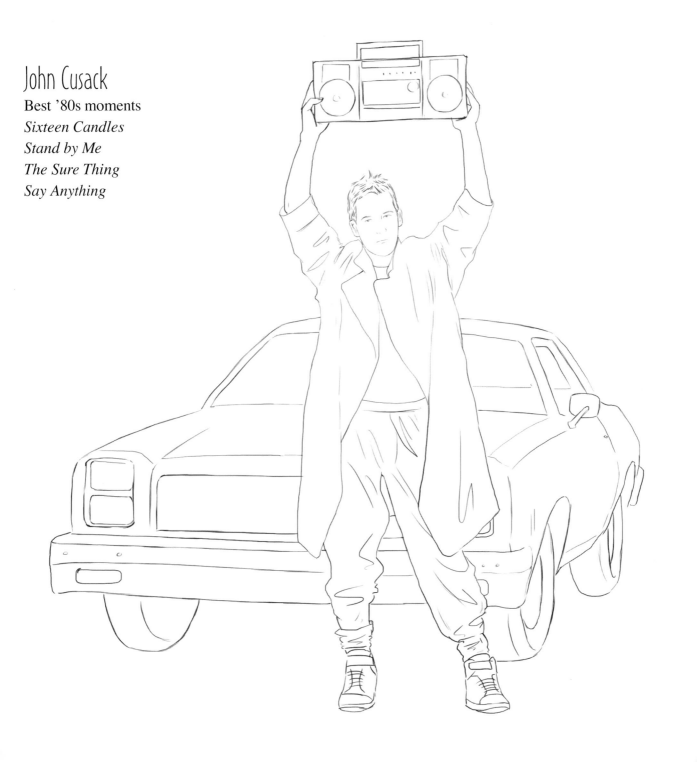

John Cusack

Best '80s moments

Sixteen Candles
Stand by Me
The Sure Thing
Say Anything

Michael J. Fox
Best '80s moments
Family Ties
Back to the Future
Teen Wolf
The Secret of My Succe$s

Tom Selleck

Best '80s moments
Magum P. I.
Three Men and a Baby
Her Alibi

MATT DAMON

Matt Damon shot to fame in 1997 with *Good Will Hunting*, which he co-wrote with Ben Affleck, winning them the Academy Award™ for Best Screenplay. Matt was off to a good start in Hollywood and it wasn't too long before he played one of the best-loved action heroes of all time, Jason Bourne.

Guess the names of these Matt Damon films!

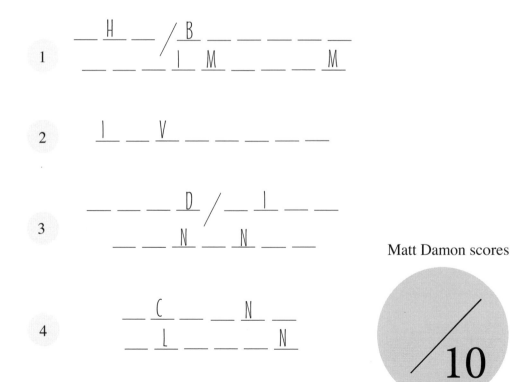

1 _ H _ _ / B _ _ _ _ _ _
   _ _ _ _ I M _ _ _ M

2 I _ V _ _ _ _ _ _

3 _ _ _ D / _ I _ _
   _ _ N _ N _ _

4 _ C _ _ N _
   _ L _ _ _ N

Matt Damon scores

/10

KEANU REEVES

My pet peeve is Keanu Reeves,
Not my cat's fleas,
Not when I sneeze,
Not my husband's addiction to cheese,
Nor when I'm out in a freezing, cold breeze,
Or that silly walk by that silly John Cleese,
Not when my allergy's making me wheeze,
Or when my duvet stinks and I'm out of Febreze,
Not when my hair looks like crap and I'm teased,
Or when I trip and fall and graze my knees.
No, my pet peeve is Keanu Reeves,
And right at the end of his movies – when he leaves :-(

Keanu Reeves practises **Buddhism**, which uses methods such as meditation as a means of changing oneself in order to develop the qualities of awareness, kindness and wisdom.
Sounds good! Wanna try it?

I give Keanu Reeves / 10

ROBERT DOWNEY JR.

If I were advertising RDJ on a billboard, his slogan would be

ROBERT DOWNEY JUNIOR MAKES OTHER MEN LOOK PUNIER!

If there were a *Colour Me Swooooon* People's Choice Award, it would most certainly go to this guy. Women of all ages adore him; men admire and want to be best buddies with him. The fact that he's had his ups and downs, his embarrassments and even his rock bottoms just add to his character, making him lovable and ever-so-slightly crazy. Despite his troubles, he's played some fantastic roles and was recently outstanding in Guy Ritchie's *Sherlock Holmes*.

The *Colour Me Swooooon* People's Choice Award I give Robert is Ultimate Iron Man. What award would you give him?

....

Robert Downey Jr. scores 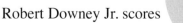  10

JOHNNY DEPP

Checking out Johnny Depp's profile on IMDb is utterly exhausting. Since starring in the TV version of *21 Jump Street* in the 1980s, he has played more weirdos than he has had fiancées* and he's barely had time to be an ordinary guy.

His most famous character has to be Captain Jack Sparrow, who Depp says he based on Keith Richards and Pepé Le Pew.

Voulez-vous coucher avec moi ce soir?

Johnny spends much of his time in France and loves pirates, so I bet if you colour this parrot, stick it on your shoulder and learn the only French pick-up line anyone ever needs to know, you'll be Johnny Depp's next fiancée before he can say "Shiver Me Timbers!"

I'd like to score Johnny Depp /10

* Lori Depp, Sherilyn Fenn, Kate Moss, Jennifer Grey and Winona Ryder.

ROBERT PATTINSON VS. TAYLOR LAUTNER

Some people might say that it's only acceptable to love Robert Pattinson *or* Taylor Lautner. It *has* to be either/or, you can't have both. In this book, they compete against each other. The winner gets coloured in beautifully; use your best felt-tips and don't go over the lines. The loser, however, gets a stupid moustache and glasses scribbled all over him and you get your cat to pee on the page.

Are you ready?

☐ Yes, then let's get started.

☐ No. Then why are you even here? Come back when you're prepared to pick sides.

Robert Pattinson is coming over for dinner. What do you cook for him?

A   Cream of porcini mushroom soup with homemade ciabatta, followed by sirloin steak, served with garlic mashed potatoes, asparagus and a red wine *jus*, and, for dessert, vanilla *panna cotta* with a raspberry coulis.

B   Nothing. I surprise him with a table at his favourite restaurant instead.

C   I see what's in the kitchen and end up giving him some cereal that's past its sell-by date.

Taylor Lautner asks you out to the movies and you can't make it. What's your excuse?

A   I can't sit next to you because you stink.

B   I have some TV to catch up on.

C   I am taking part in this charity event to help raise awareness for dyslexic cats. Why don't you come along?

I give RPatz

You're enjoying a great picnic in the woods when you spot two hungry bears ferociously attacking RPatz and Taylor. Luckily, you have a rifle by your side but it only has one bullet. What do you do?

A   Shoot the bear that is attacking RPatz, then run off screaming.

B   Drop the rifle and run off screaming.

C   Run over to the bear that is attacking Taylor, beat it over the head with the rifle to knock it unconscious but so that it will awake unhurt, pick Taylor up in your arms and carry him to safety – while screaming.

Common sense has set in and you have realised that you can only stalk one more celebrity before being locked up behind bars. Who do you choose?

A   I choose Robert Pattinson because he looks like he neeeeeeeeds me!!

B   No one. I choose life and decide to quit stalking for good, while at the same time working on forging real relationships rather than imaginary ones with celebrities who don't even know I exist. I also marry my cat.

C   I really want to stalk Taylor Lautner, but I resist because I don't want to hurt him. If you love someone, set them free, etc.

So what did you score?
If you answered mostly As, RPatz is your man; get your felt-tips out and go for it.
If you answered mostly Bs, you're undecided – toss a coin.
If you answered mostly Cs, you're in love with Taylor Lautner and you should get your eyes tested.

10

THE QUIRKY HOT TEAM!

Many of the guys in this book are what we would describe as "perfect". Their noses are in perfect proportion to their face, their legs are the correct length and every hair on their body is in just the right place.

But some guys just weren't built like that. There's something slightly quirky about them ...

AND I LOVE THAT!

This section celebrates men who thrive on being a little bit different from the rest. They attract terrific roles and, whether they are really cute, hilarious, incredibly intelligent, or just completely insane, something about them just works.

Que Cera Cera /10

I score Adam Driver /10

Andrew Garfield would get /10

Segel scores /10

I score Chris O'Dowd /10

Michael Cera

His finest moments
Superbad
Youth in Revolt
Arrested Development
Juno

Adam Driver

His finest moments
J. Edgar
Girls
Lincoln

Andrew Garfield

His finest moments

Never Let Me Go

The Social Network

The Amazing Spiderman

Jason Segel

His finest moments

Knocked Up

How I Met Your Mother

Forgetting Sarah Marshall

Bad Teacher

The Five-Year Engagement

Chris O'Dowd

His finest moments
The IT Crowd
Gulliver's Travels
Bridesmaids
Girls

JON HAMM

I would like to have Jon Hamm.
I would like him in a house, as my spouse.
In a box, wearing nothing but socks.
I would like him in a tree. If I had Jon Hamm I would not let him be.
In the park, in the dark.
On some bread, in my bed.
I would like him on my table. I'll keep him there if I am able.
On the floor! On the floor! Would I like him on the floor?
Yes, I'd like that even more.
I would like him in a car. I'd love him up and drive him far.
I would like him here or there. I'd squish him like a teddy bear.
I would like to have Jon Hamm.
Can I? Can I? Say I can!

If *you* would like to have Jon Hamm, ADVERTISE YOURSELF!
Impress him with your best *Mad Men*-style poster ad.
Give yourself a catchy slogan and pose in a figure-hugging outfit
while holding a stiff drink.

I would like to give Jon Hamm /10

JIM MORRISON

Not many men can wear leather trousers and pull it off ... but Jim could. And he did. *A lot.*

I can't begin to imagine what those leather trousers must have smelt like after a gig. But it doesn't matter. Jim Morrison oozed raw animal charisma like no other man of his era did. His musical performances were mesmerising and he relied on his pure, genuine talent to enthral audiences.

Following a chaotic and unsaintly existence, Jim sadly broke through to the other side in 1971. Many a musician (and student) have tried to emulate him since, but none has been able to replicate the leather-trouser look anywhere as good as he did.

RIP Jim Morrison

To celebrate Jim Morrison, put on your floatiest maxi-dress, wear pretty flowers in your hair, and groove to *The Doors*, immerse yourself totally in sixties hippiedom. Go barefoot, love everyone, twirl around and stick two fingers up to The Man. It's what he would have wanted.

I love Jim Morrison this many times / 10

RUSSELL BRAND

The thing with Russell Brand
is that he's rarely bland,
and that the laughter's never canned –
Because he's nuts.

He's unpredictable,
Sometimes mentally unwell
With way too much hair gel –
Because he's nuts.

Sarah Marshall was remembered,
Ceremonies were attended,
and celebrities offended –
Because he's nuts.

With his skinny jeans and blouse
My passion can't be housed,
and he gets me all aroused –
Because *I'm* nuts!

The thing I love to hate about Russell is his

....

Russell Brand gets a whopping

10

RICHARD GERE

Richard Gere rescues women. Whether they're a humble factory worker or a big-mouthed prostitute, he whisks them off to a land of happiness. It's what he does best and for that we adore and applaud him.

The first time I was blown away with romance (and jealousy) was while watching *An Officer and a Gentleman* and desperately wishing to be Debra Winger being carried out by the dashing Marine. I longed for Richard Gere to rescue me some day. How about you?

I would like Richard Gere to rescue me from

....

I would like him to turn up on a

....

And take me to

....

Where we will live happily ever after doing

....

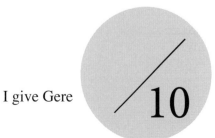

I give Gere 10

JUDE LAW

This cheeky English chap shot to international fame sashaying around in skimpy shorts during *The Talented Mr. Ripley*. But when he played notorious womaniser *Alfie*, I sat up and took notice.

His face is, without doubt, beautiful – with piercing eyes, a perfect jawline, and a chin dimple cuter than Bambi.

Do you know how to write a limerick? They consist of five lines, with lines one, two, and five rhyming together and lines three and four rhyming together. The key is to keep them short and silly. Try to write a love limerick about Jude Law.
Here's my example:

There was a young man named Jude Law
Who made all the ladies go "PHWOAARR"
Terrific at breeding
Now his hairline's receding
But I'm sure we are gagging for more.

Jude scores / 10

WILL SMITH

Anyone who names their albums *Big Willie Style* and *Willennium* is all right with me! I have sought many people's opinions regarding the men in this book and Will is the only guy who has received a unanimous "YES" from everyone. There is nothing remotely pretentious about him; he's fun, charismatic, humble, loyal and down-to-earth. He can act, he can sing, he can dance and he looks great in the buff.

Everyone should know how to rap! Try this one to the tune from *The Fresh Prince of Bel-Air* (then try writing your own verse!):

> Well, this is a story 'bout a guy named Will Smith
> A man who the girls wanna get jiggy with
> When he's a man in black or Muhammad Ali
> They're thinking, "Why's Will not in pursuit of me!?"
> Since *Big Willie Style* their life's been enriched
> Only trouble is Will's already hitched
> So, just sit back, chillax with some Jerry & Ben's
> And give him some colour with your best felt tip pens!

Lyrics by Lil' Mellyelliott

Will scores **10**

MICHAEL FASSBENDER

Imagine you're in a club – maybe an after-party following an awards ceremony. Michael Fassbender is standing at the bar; he is surrounded by glamorous people trying to impress him. How are *you* going to stand out and win his affections?

By speaking German, that's how.

I learned from watching *Inglourious Basterds* that Michael Fassbender can speak fluent German (not well enough to prevent him from being shot, but well enough to get chatted up by you).

Learn these fail-safe chat-up lines in German and within seconds you'll have Michael wrapped around your little finger!

Kommst du hier oftmals?
Do you come here often?

Michael, hast du gepupst oder hast du mich nur verknallt?
Michael, did you fart? Because you blow me away!

Mensch! Du siehst genauso aus wie meinen nächsten Freund!
Oh wow! You look just like my next boyfriend!

Michael Fassbender deserves  10

NICHOLAS HOULT

Watching *About a Boy* in 2002, it was difficult to imagine that its star would grow up to be one of Britain's hottest young men.

Long gone is the fringe and bad-fitting charity shop trousers, making way for a super-cool action hero with jeans that fit just right, having his hair combed by supermodels in Tom Ford campaigns.

Along with Julianne Moore, Nicholas and his fluffy sweater completely stole the show in *A Single Man*, and despite his growing international success he still comes across as slightly unsure and bewildered but completely adorable.

Draw Nicholas Hoult's character in *About a Boy* (don't worry if it's not very good). Listen to the fantastic soundtrack at the same time!

I give Nicholas / 10

Marcus Brewer

ORIGINAL
SWOONEES

PAUL NEWMAN

1925–2008
He was the best thing in:

Butch Cassidy and
   The Sundance Kid
Cool Hand Luke
The Sting
The Hustler

STEVE McQUEEN

1930–1980
He was the best thing in:

The Great Escape
Bullitt
Towering Inferno
The Thomas Crown Affair

Originally from Yorkshire, in northern England, I studied at the Royal College of Art in London and now live on the South Coast, in Hastings.

A few years ago I started making contemporary colouring books, paper dolls, temporary tattoos and prints, which I sell on my website www.ilovemel.me.

I think being a grown-up should be fun!

Did you get stuck on any of the puzzles?

☐ No, I'm a genius.

☐ Yes, and it's preventing me from sleeping at night. I need some answers.

Then go here!

Please tweet me your colouring efforts!
@mellyelliott